Index

Food from Farm to Home

By the Same Author

AUTOMOBILES, PAST AND PRESENT
BREAD, THE STAFF OF LIFE
CLOTH FROM FIBER TO FABRIC
HARVEST OF THE SEA
THE MAGIC OF PAPER
THE MARVEL OF GLASS
MEAT FROM RANCH TO TABLE
OIL, TODAY'S BLACK MAGIC
PLASTICS, THE MAN-MADE MIRACLE
RUBBER, NATURAL AND SYNTHETIC
SALT, SUGAR, AND SPICE
TIMBER! *Farming Our Forests*
UNDERGROUND RICHES, *The Story of Mining*
VOLCANO!
WONDER WORKER, *The Story of Electricity*

Food
FROM FARM TO HOME

written and illustrated by
Walter Buehr

William Morrow and Company
New York

I wish to express my gratitude for the help and professional knowledge extended to me by Mr. Leonard Warner and by other members of the staff of the American Farm Bureau Federation. They supplied me with the latest information on modern farming, on poultry and livestock raising, on dairying, fruit and vegetable production, farm building design, and mechanized planting and harvesting. Their suggestions of what the farm of the twenty-first century may be like were especially helpful, and they show how the farmer of the future may be able to conquer the problems of a runaway world population. I felt fortunate indeed to have such accurate, up-to-date, and detailed material at my disposal.

Walter Buehr
July, 1969

Contents

Farming for All

In the early 1900's, almost everyone had a grandfather or an uncle who lived on a farm. During summer visits children searched for eggs in nests that the wily hens had hidden in the bushes near the barnyard. They watched the cows being milked, gathered peaches from the heavily burdened trees, or picked blueberries for a delicious pie.

If roast chicken were planned for Sunday dinner, first a fat hen had to be caught and killed.

Then she had to be plucked and cleaned before she was ready for the oven. The corn patch provided the ears for tender, steaming corn on the cob, which were slathered with an ample supply of butter from the springhouse.

Today, however, people generally see their food only as it appears in the supermarket. There dozens of packaged products, from cornflakes to instant mashed potatoes, line the shelves. Long refrigerator bins overflow with bacon, ham, beef and lamb roasts, pork and veal chops, rows of plump chickens and turkeys, all carefully cleaned, boned, or trimmed, and neatly wrapped in cellophane. Fresh strawberries, California lettuce, grapes, avocados, and ruddy tomatoes are available all year round. How these foods are grown or raised is generally unknown.

Nevertheless, the facts about modern food production are impressive and should not be taken for granted. Today the farmer is able to choose from a remarkable assortment of ingenious machinery to help him grow his crops.

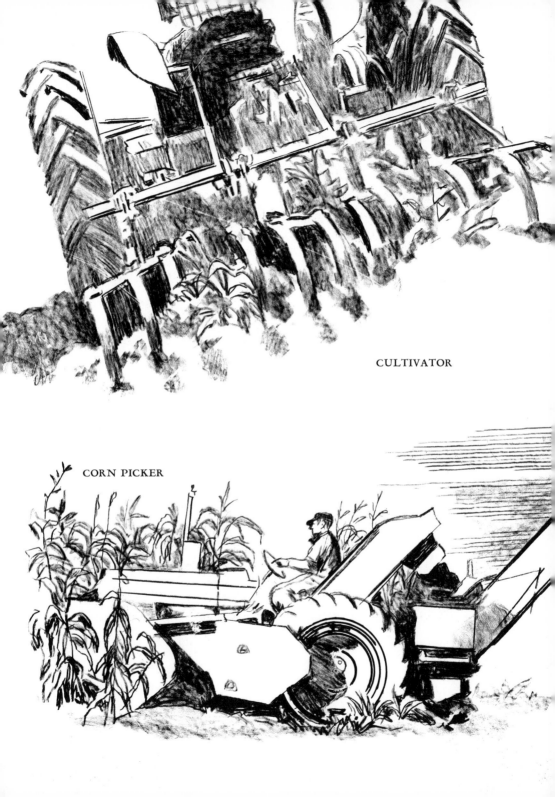

CULTIVATOR

CORN PICKER

There is the farm tractor, the gang plow, the seed drill, and the combine, as well as the great trailer and refrigerator trucks, which enable the farmer to reach a wide market. To equip an average farm he must invest at least $125,000.

The farmer has to invest time as well as money. Many crops and animals require years of care before they can produce income. It takes two and a half years before a cow can have a calf of her own and begin to pay back her "board" in the shape of milk, veal, or beef. An orchard must be cultivated, pruned, sprayed, and fertilized for years before the first box of fruit can be picked and shipped to market.

Although farmers comprise less than six percent of our population, today each one grows enough to feed forty-one persons. How he accomplishes this feat is a story of interest to all.

The Growth of Farms

In the early eighteenth century the American colonies were strung along a narrow strip of the Eastern seaboard from Maine to the Carolinas on the heavily forested slopes east of the Allegheny Mountains. There were only a few small towns, like Boston, New York, and Philadelphia, which owed their existence to good harbors.

The townspeople who had jobs were the shopkeepers and craftsmen like tailors, shoemakers, blacksmiths, carpenters, and masons. Most of them raised their own vegetables, kept chickens, cows, and pigs, spun their own yarn, and wove the cloth to make their clothes. The rest of the colonists lived entirely off the land.

The young pioneer and his bride often began

14

their life together by trudging westward from some backwoods settlement into the silent, virgin forest, leading a horse or ox loaded with a pack of bedding, pots and pans, gunpowder, and lead for making bullets. The only tools they carried were a rifle, ax, and hoe. With them, the

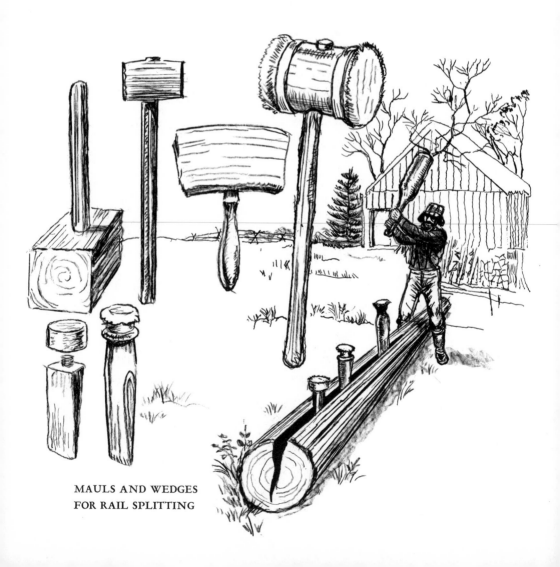

MAULS AND WEDGES
FOR RAIL SPLITTING

new farmer shot game for the cooking pot and planted his seeds and Indian corn. He chopped down and cleared the trees from a patch of land and built a rough lean-to for shelter.

The pelts of the beaver and other animals he shot and trapped he traded for a plow and cart, a flock of chickens, a cow, and a litter of pigs. Presently the farmer cut down more trees and built a one-room log cabin with a fireplace, turning the lean-to into a stable. He planted other crops among the stumps and great boulders of the newly cleared fields, until he had time to haul the rocks from the fields on a homemade

17

COLONIAL PLOWS

stoneboat and to wrench out and burn the stumps. Then at last he was able to plow and harrow his fields instead of chopping the ground with a hoe.

Life on a colonial farm was hard; plowing,

18

planting, harrowing, weeding, and harvesting were done mostly by hand or with a horse or ox. The chores were endless. In winter the farmer repaired broken tools, rehung doors, built butter churns or apple parers, and hammered out horseshoes, hinges, and nails on his small forge.

The backwoodsman made his own soap by dripping lye from wood ashes into kettles of boiling hog fat. He salted down pork for the summer, shelled corn, made cider from apples gathered from his orchard of trees brought from England, and collected maple syrup or sugar by boiling sap from sugar maples in a huge iron kettle.

Every farm grew flax to make linen and thread, and raised a flock of sheep, whose wool the farmwife spun and wove into homespun on the spinning wheel. After the fall slaughtering, the hides of the cattle and hogs were piled into the wagon and brought to the tanner. Then the traveling shoemaker, who visited for a week every year to outfit the entire family, made them into harnesses, boots, shoes, and mittens.

The colonists brought with them from England
all the seeds of the cereal grains except corn, or

maize, which they learned how to grow from the Indians, who cultivated corn patches in clearings in the forest. They parched the kernels over a fire, storing them against winter famine. The Indians also showed the white settlers how to fertilize maize, by putting several dead fish around the roots of every hill of corn.

Luckily for the pioneer farmer, many of the insects prevalent today had not yet arrived on our shores, and for a while he could raise fruits and vegetables without much damage from pests and diseases. He had to contend, however, with deer, rabbits, woodchucks, bears, and raccoons, as well as crows, blackbirds, and other birds, all of whom were eager to share the fruits of his toil.

The biggest problem of the frontier farmer, however, was finding a market for what he raised. He had enormous difficulty getting a wagonload of crops to town or the mill over the few available roads. Even in the best weather they were rough and potholed, and in rain or snow they became completely impassable. Transporting large quantities of wheat or corn from farms a long way from town was such a task that many farmers set up stills and turned their grain into whiskey, which was easier to ship and was welcomed by the hard-drinking people of that day.

Along the coast and on the large rivers, like the Hudson and the Delaware, sailing vessels carried much farm produce to the towns, and in the early nineteenth century canalboats did a brisk freight business over the newly dug canals. Still, water transport could not reach many of the farms, which were as isolated as before.

Then, in the late nineteenth and early twentieth centuries, new advancements changed American farm life enormously for the better. In 1897, United States Rural Free Delivery mail routes were established, and the farmer's mail was delivered directly from the village post office to his mailbox by buggy or wagon. Soon rural residents were receiving letters, newspapers, magazines, catalogs, and books, in addition to

shoes, nursery stock, and machinery parts, as
promptly as did their city cousins. The farmer
also could keep abreast of farm prices, crop re-
ports, agricultural bulletins, and world news.

Further contact with the outside world was established with the invention of the telephone by Alexander Graham Bell. The early magneto phones were crude, and they had to be cranked by hand to ring a bell, which sounded on each instrument along the line. Furthermore, since anybody on the line could listen in to all conversations, every farmwife kept informed of local gossip. Rural telephones had other problems too. Subscribers were far apart, and the long lines of cable often were brought down by falling trees, ice, or winds. Most companies, moreover, did not have enough capital to keep their equipment in good condition. By the 1940's, however, rural service was much improved, and the old magneto phones were supplanted by modern dial service.

American farmers were among the first to take advantage of radio, and many of them installed the early battery-powered sets before power lines reached their farms. Especially in the West, on the large ranches and farms, farmers carried small two-way radio sets in their cars, trucks, and trac-

tors, so that they were always in contact with a central station at the farm office.

The coming of electricity also revolutionized the farmer's life. In the home it provided running water, heated the flatiron, lighted the lamps, and powered the deepfreeze, refrigerator, and furnace. In the outbuildings and barns electricity lessened the farmer's chores immeasurably. Feed and silage were distributed automatically by electric motors to the cattle, pigs, and poultry. Baby chicks were hatched in electric incubators, and electric brooders kept them warm and snug until they matured. Barns, milking rooms, poultry sheds, pigpens, and storage sheds were flooded with light at night, and well-equipped machine shops with power tools enabled the farmer to build and repair buildings. Electric power lifted the burden of hand labor from the farmer's back and enabled him to operate his farm profitably with fewer hired hands and pay higher wages for those remaining.

Improvements in transportation helped tie the

farmer to the rest of the country. In less than fifty years the railroads bound together with a steel web most of the United States east of the Mississippi. No more was the farmwife's shopping restricted to the wares carried by the wandering peddler. Every small town on a branch railroad now had a direct connection with the big cities, and newspapers, ladies' fashions, cream separators, and sewing machines eventually reached the farthest backwoods farm. Freight cars also carried cattle and hogs, grain and cotton to commission men in the cities, freeing the farmers from the domination of small-town buyers.

The Texas cattlemen realized that if they could get their herds north to the railheads in Kansas, the cattle could be shipped to the big cities, which were clamoring for meat. Groups of ranchers organized trail drives and herded thousands of Longhorns over the plains, fording rivers, and fighting off Indian raids and packs of wolves. After being loaded into cattle cars, the

cattle headed for the slaughterhouse in Kansas
City or Chicago.

While the fantastic increase in railroad mileage during the late nineteenth century opened up many thousands of acres of good land to farming, the farmer still had difficulty bringing his crops from the barn to the grain elevator or railroad siding, for the country dirt roads were extremely poor. Farmers could not afford to build roads properly and level steep ridges, dig

ditches, and build culverts and good bridges. The roads, therefore, were quagmires of mud in the spring, choked with dust in summer, and piled high with snowdrifts in winter. Jolting wagons could travel on them only at a rate of two miles an hour.

In the first quarter of the twentieth century, the coming of the automobile, which simply could not operate over the old-fashioned dirt road, created a demand for improved highways. Suddenly a great surge of road building swept over the country from ocean to ocean.

At first, many farmers resisted the new road construction, because they feared the cars would kill their chickens and frighten their cows. Some even buried scrap metal in the roads to puncture car tires, and others charged motorists outrageous prices to tow cars that were bogged down in mudholes with their teams of horses. Soon, however, they awoke to the enormous advantages paved roads brought them. Now the jobs of hauling feed and other farm supplies, carrying crops to the elevator, and transporting cattle and pigs to the packinghouse were easier than ever before.

Improvements in transportation continued through the years and are still being developed today. The huge refrigerator trailer truck has brought vast new markets within the farmer's reach. The lettuce grower of California, the onion raiser of Texas, the fruit farmer of California and Florida, and the tomato cropper of Georgia can load his ripening crop into a chilled trailer and within hours it will be delivered to a supermarket chain hundreds of miles away.

Additional markets have been opened up by air cargo. Since the 1950's, the airlines have been shipping more and more food products. Tall stacks of cartons filled with perishable fruits and vegetables are loaded every day into giant cargo planes, and fresh strawberries, grapes, broccoli, tomatoes, and berries are flown from the farms of California, Texas, the Gulf states, and Florida to supermarkets in the East, the Midwest, and even abroad. Poultrymen ship thousands of baby chicks to egg producers, and breeders send prize calves, pigs, and breeding bulls by air to insure their quick, safe arrival.

Major Farm Products

U. S. 1528117

HAY

Hay is still one of the most important crops on the American farm, because it is a main source of food for livestock during the winter. In the old days, it was cut with a scythe, raked into

ROOFED
HAYSTACKS

EARLY FARM TOOLS

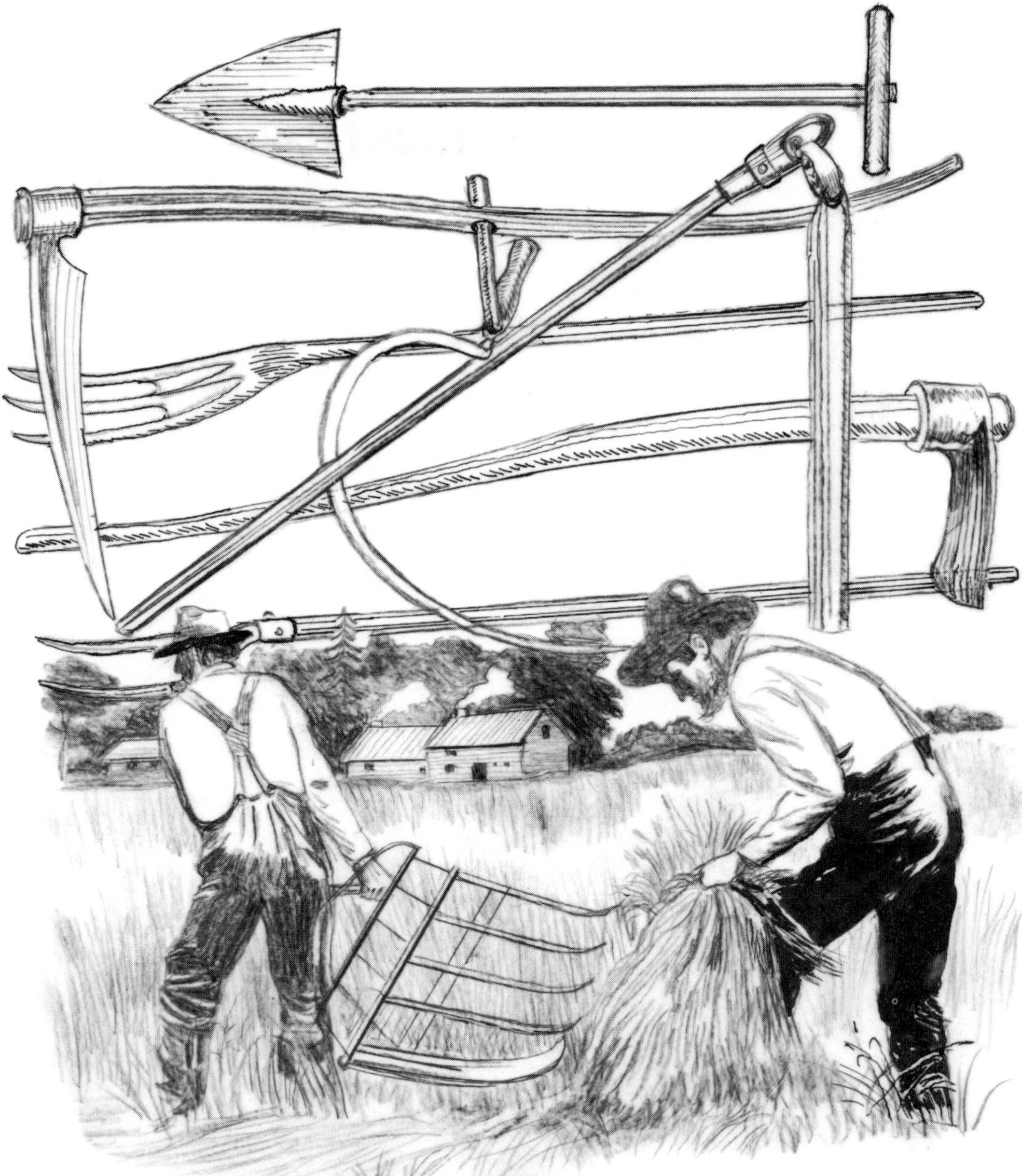

windrows with a hand rake, then heaved with a pitchfork into towering mounds aboard a hay wagon, and trundled to the barn. There it was transferred to the cavernous hayloft and compactly stowed. Haying was always an anxious time. Since wet hay will molder and spoil when stored, it had to be got under cover before a sudden rainstorm drenched it.

As haying was hard, hurried work, early inventors of farm machines tried to lessen its toil and strain. In the middle 1800's, the horse-drawn mower with a hinged cutter bar, the horse rake,

HORSE RAKE

**SELF-PROPELLED FORAGE HARVESTER
CHOPPING ALFALFA**

and the mechanical hay-loader replaced the scythe, the hand rake, and the pitchfork. Horse forks lifted the loose stacks of hay up into the haymow, and balers compressed it, to make handling easier. A forage harvester, developed in 1936, made grass silage possible. Improved balers, bale throwers, hay conditioners, and driers enabled the farmer to gather and store his hay crop in better condition and with much less hired labor. The haystack, the haymow, and the towering hay wagon soon became things of the past.

38

GRAIN

Believed to be one of the first crops cultivated by man, grain provides half the calories of the world's three billion inhabitants. It is eaten either as whole kernels or as flour, and is also used for livestock and poultry feed, and, industrially, for making alcohol and starch.

Wheat is one of the two chief grains, and there are two basic types: hard and soft. Soft wheat is used for making bread, cookies, crackers, pastries, and cake mixes. Hard wheat, which is grown in the West and Northwest, is found in our packaged bread because it improves quality. Spaghetti, macaroni, and noodles are made from a hard wheat called durum wheat.

Corn, the other chief grain, is eaten as corn meal and hominy grits, while cornstarch produces such byproducts as corn syrup and corn oil. Most of our corn, however, is used as stock food for our hogs and cattle.

As the nineteenth-century farmers moved westward, they began to plant bigger crops of grain on the rich Midwestern soil, and the old hand methods they had used on the small, rocky fields in the East became too slow. Then Cyrus H. McCormick developed a mechanical reaper and demonstrated it successfully in 1831. Now the farmer no longer had to harvest his grain with a scythe. Several years later, in 1841, a Nantucket mechanic named Obed Hussey patented a reaper. As a team of horses pulled the wheeled machine up and down the field, triangular knives

FIRST REAPER
DEMONSTRATED BY
CYRUS H. MCCORMICK

attached to a horizontal bar vibrated between metal fingers and cut the stalks, while another device bound the cut grain into sheaves. By 1848, McCormick completed an improved version of the reaper, which was fitted with an automatic rake to eliminate the extra sheaf binder.

41

Soon his factory in Chicago was selling hundreds of them.

The early farmers had only two ways of separating the kernels of grain from the stalks. One was to spread the sheaves in a circle on the threshing floor in the barn and drive oxen or horses around and around over them. The other was to beat out the kernels by striking them with a hinged pole, called a flail. Afterward, the har-

HAND FLAIL

TREADMILL THRESHER

vesters tossed the grain high in the air with a pitchfork on a windy day and let the wind carry away the chaff, while the heavier kernels fell to the floor. Then they were shoveled into sacks.

Many ingenious inventions improved the methods of threshing. One type of flail had an

43

HORSE-DRAWN COMBINE

iron cylinder armed with whirling teeth in a concave drum. Another device that shook the grain from the stalks and winnowed the chaff was powered by a team of horses harnessed to a treadmill. Later a much larger thresher, the sweep horsepower machine, with a team of

44

horses hitched to each set of revolving arms, was able to handle much more grain than the treadmill.

Manufacturers also began displaying steel cultivators, headers, and seeders, some of them designed for the huge Kansas and Nebraska

STEAM TRACTION ENGINE

farms. Giant machines, drawn by dozens of horses, crawled steadily across the seas of waving golden grain, clipping off the plump heads and leaving the straw to rot and be plowed under. Often the header was combined with a thresher in one gigantic machine, which cut and threshed the grain and poured it into bags, ready for the flour mill.

Presently the heavy, clumsy steam traction

engine, a country version of the railroad loco-
motive, replaced horsepower. During the
summer harvest season, the engine, puffing
clouds of black smoke, rumbled up the drive-
way of a farm. Then the neighbors, who had
been awaiting its arrival, gathered to lend a
hand in return for help with their own crop.
Dragging behind it a big threshing machine, the
engine got up steam. The long drive belt began
to slap as the sheaves of grain were fed into the
spiked throat of the thresher and the great sieves
vibrated to and fro, shaking the golden kernels
free and tumbling them into the grain sacks.

The steam traction engine, however, was slow
and needed such a large crew it was costly to
operate. By 1903, gasoline-powered tractors were

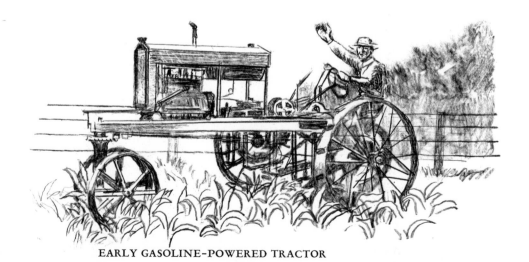

EARLY GASOLINE-POWERED TRACTOR

COMBINE

being turned out. The massive, rough-riding, steel-rimmed wheels were replaced with rubber tires in 1932.

Today corn planters plant as many as eight rows of corn at once. When it is ripe, the corn picker and sheller rumble along, shucking the golden ears and shelling the kernels. Giant combines, driven by one man, whizz through vast

50

fields of grain, clipping off the ripe heads, threshing them, and dropping the plump kernels into
trucks ready for the mill or granary. They accom-
plish more in a few hours than the old-fashioned
harvesting crew with a machine drawn by many
teams of horses did in a week.

The United States now produces about 220
million tons of grain every year, one fifth of

51

which is exported. This total includes 100 million tons of corn, which represents about half of the world production.

MULTIPLE-ROW CORN PICKER AND SHELLER

FRUITS AND VEGETABLES

Fruits and vegetables were always difficult to harvest, but by the 1960's the shortage of labor began to become serious. American farm workers disliked stoop labor, and they expected wages as high as those of factory workers. Foreign laborers, mostly Mexicans in the West and Southwest, no longer were permitted to cross the border at harvesttime to work, and wetbacks, Mexicans who waded across the Rio Grande to enter the United States illegally, were sent back.

Crops such as cherries, tomatoes, and even apples were in danger of costing so much to market that they would price themselves off the grocers' shelves. For this reason, plant breeders and mechanical engineers began studying the problem of picking the crops mechanically.

Each needed a different solution. For some, changing the qualities of the vegetable itself was necessary before a machine could be built to pick it. For instance, the standard tomato was found to be too large, round, and soft, and too low-growing for mechanical picking, so plant breeders developed a new kind of tomato. It grew higher off the ground and had smaller, firmer fruit and a long shape. Within ten years the harvesting of almost the entire California tomato crop was mechanized, and the housewife could buy her tomato products at reasonable prices. Snap beans, lima beans, cabbages, potatoes, carrots, onions, spinach, and even pickles were redesigned, often many times, before they could be machine picked quickly and without damage.

The fruit raiser had even greater troubles than the vegetable farmer. Cherries, apples, blackberries, cranberries, and raspberries, among others, were difficult to pick, easily bruised, and expensive to inspect and pack. Further problems were created by the rising labor costs and the constantly increasing difficulty of assembling the large numbers of pickers needed during the short harvest season. Growers began to fear that fruit pies soon would be only a memory.

Then one hot summer day, in 1959, a weird-looking machine trundled up to a tree in a Michigan cherry orchard laden with tart ruby fruit. A mechanical arm was fastened to a limb and shook the tree violently, dropping a rain of cherries into a net stretched out below. This machine was the first to replace hand picking, although it was far from perfect. Today one machine with a five-man crew can pick as many cherries as a hundred hand pickers can. Mechanization has cut the cost of harvesting cherries to only two and a half cents a pound.

Other steps in preparing the fruit for market are done mechanically. The cherries pass by an electric sorter, where photoelectric cells scan them at the rate of 5000 a minute and reject imperfect ones. A rotating knife blade set directly above a moving belt loaded with cherries snips off the stems.

Today research men also are concerned with pruning, propagation, spraying, and with protecting trees and fruit from disease and pests. One of the costliest chores in an apple orchard is thinning the number of apples on a tree; too many will affect the size, color, and quality of the fruit and also prevent the tree from bearing every year. The modern orchardist sprays the young fruit with a growth-regulating chemical that thins the crop automatically and another that delays the maturing of the fruit, so apples will not drop to the ground before picking time.

EGGS AND POULTRY

At first the farmwife was in charge of raising poultry, and her methods were apt to be haphazard. The fowls had the run of the barnyard, roosting in trees or under the eaves of sheds at night. They picked up what food they could from the ground, table scraps from the kitchen, and spilled grain from the mangers, and they made nests in the bushes, where their eggs had to be searched out before they spoiled. When the hens grew broody, they were penned up on a setting of eggs until they hatched. Then for several weeks the mother hen fussily led her fluffy yellow chicks around the barnyard, scratching up worms and insects until they were old enough to fend for themselves.

Today producing eggs is strictly a matter of costs and efficiency; the romance of poultry raising is gone. It has developed slowly from a sideline into an important business, each step of which is carried on by a specialist in his field.

The primary breeder supplies eggs and chicks to commercial hatcheries. His aim is to build top quality into his stock. Each breeder is known for a special type of egg or chick, which has a trademarked name that cannot be imitated by other breeders. He employs experts—geneticists, veterinarians, and bacteriologists—who constantly are testing and experimenting to make sure his chicks are strong and healthy.

The hatchery produces large numbers of day-old chicks from eggs supplied by the breeder.

The egg producer raises these chicks until they become pullets. After about a year the laying hens are sold off to the butcher, and a new batch of pullets is purchased from another specialist who supplies replacement birds, or the egg producer raises his own.

A poultry farm run by a single family using no hired help can handle from ten to fifteen thousand birds if the plant is up-to-date. There are flocks of much larger size. Egg City in California and several other farms boast of flocks of over a million birds, but some egg producers are beginning to feel that such large numbers might bring on disease problems and result in less efficient management control.

The henhouse of a modern poultry farm is a windowless, brightly lit building, usually only one story high. Thousands of clucking birds entirely fill the vast floor. All of them are the same size and color, since producers generally separate different breeds.

The ratproof concrete floors are easy to clean

and are spread with corn husks, peanut shells, wood chips, or other litter. Water troughs scattered throughout the room are kept filled automatically, and they are designed so the hens cannot spill much water on the floor.

Their feed, freshly mixed every day or two, is delivered from the mill in a big tank truck and pumped pneumatically into a huge hopper at the end of each henhouse, from which it is distributed through pipes by a worm gear to all the feed troughs. The feed consists of ground-up meal containing a scientific mixture of cornmeal, soybean meal, bone meal, fish meal, and grain from distilleries. About four pounds of feed are needed to produce a dozen eggs.

Some farms supply recorded music to soothe the birds and make them more eager to lay. Here and there infrared heat lamps heat the floor below, where chilly hens huddle for extra warmth. Henhouses in moderate climates usually are not heated, but during hot weather they are ventilated and cooled by suction fans.

There are no roosts; the birds simply squat on
the floor. Along each side of the building is a
long row of nests, raised slightly from the floor,

into which a steady stream of hens enter by
ramps to make their contributions. The bottom
of each nest is part of an endless belt, which

moves slowly at just the right speed to permit the hen to lay her egg and depart before she is bumped against the partition of the next nest. Each freshly laid egg travels to the end of the row and down into a plastic container. Then it goes to the scanner.

Here each egg is placed on a transparent belt where it is candled, a process by which a light is shined through the egg to discover cracks in the shell or blood in the yolk. Next it passes into a cleaning chamber, where it is washed and brushed, pushed through holes of graduated sizes, and dropped into a plastic container. It is stored in a fifty-five degree temperature until shipping time.

An often-asked question is whether white or brown eggs are best. In New York City white eggs generally are preferred, while in Boston the brown ones are most popular. Long ago these preferences had some basis, because then the freshest eggs sent from New Jersey farms to New York were usually white, while brown eggs came from farms in the Midwest and were therefore less choice. In Boston the eggs from nearby farms were usually brown, and white eggs came from farther away. Any poultryman will tell you that today there is absolutely no difference in eggs because of the color of their shells.

At one time there was a glut of eggs during some seasons and a scarcity at other times, so dealers bought them when they were cheap and put them in cold storage. Now, however, fresh eggs come on the market in sufficient quantities to fill the demand all through the year.

Some modern hatcheries or processors supply chicks, feed, labor, and even medical care to farmers who have poultry buildings available. They hire the farmer under a contract to raise the birds. The processors pay bonuses to those who turn in above-average production records. Both processors and farmers share special costs, due to accidents, unfavorable weather, or disease.

Not many years ago, roast turkey appeared on the dinner table only at Thanksgiving and Christmas as a special treat. Turkeys were expensive, because so many were lost through various ailments that the survivors brought high prices. Now the turkey raiser uses the scientific methods of other poultrymen and produces thousands of healthy birds at moderate prices the year round. He even has learned to grow smaller birds that will fit into an apartment-sized oven and will produce a greater percentage of white meat for those who always ask for "some of the breast, please."

MILK

It has been said that the chore of milking on the old farm, each morning and evening, drove away more men than the hard labor of plowing and harvesting. Stumbling to the barn in a freezing winter dawn, carrying a smoky lantern, the farmer cleaned out the cows' stalls, shoveled grain and hay into their feed bins, and filled their water buckets. Then he crouched against each steaming bovine flank, trying to dodge bossy's swishing tail, and spurted the milk into a bucket with stiffened fingers.

Still to follow would be the job of skimming

the cream from the pans of milk of the previous milking. Then the cream was churned into butter and cheese, and the skimmed milk was poured into the troughs of the chickens and pigs. Last all the milk containers were scoured with boiling water.

Since that time the dairy industry has changed radically. It too has become specialized; farmers no longer care for one or several cows, and milk producers seldom make butter, cheese, or ice cream, leaving that to the dairy to which they sell their milk. The modern dairy farm is planned to be as efficient and automated as possible to save the high cost of labor.

The barn itself has stalls fitted with steel stanchions, which let the cow move about considerably and lie down. In some milking rooms the stalls are elevated about three feet, so that the milker will not have to stoop, and they are set at a herringbone angle, so each cow's udder is only about three feet from the next cow's, which speeds up the milking.

The cement floors slope gently to a gutter at the rear, where litter and manure gather. At intervals, a brush cleaner and hose slide back and forth in the gutter, flushing the waste to the end of the stalls and down a hole to a manure spreader on the floor below. A shovelful of wood chips or other litter then is spread to provide a clean bed for the cows.

Each pair of stalls share a water fountain,

MANURE SPREADER

which refills itself as the cow drinks. A cement feed bin holds the cow's allotment of feed, which automatically drops into the manger just before milking time. The amount is determined by the number of pounds of milk she is giving.

The cow's rations are compounded scientifically at the mill, and they are a long way from the old-time shovelful of corn and oats. One popular ration contains steamed yellow corn, crimped oats, soybean meal, linseed meal, dried grains, corn gluten, dehydrated alfalfa meal, wheat bran, middlings, ground oats, hominy, molasses, salt, calcium carbonate, vitamin A, and irradiated yeast. In addition, each cow gets a manger of baled hay to munch on while she is being milked.

A healthy cow produces an average of forty pounds of milk a day, although some prize milkers give twice as much, and small cows, such as Jerseys, average less, but have richer milk. Milking is done almost entirely by machines today. Only cows made nervous by the milking machine or those with sore udders are hand milked.

There are many different types of milking machines, but they all work on the same principle. Four rubber tubes dangle from an electric suction pump connected by a hose to a portable small tank or, in a large dairy, to an overhead pipe leading directly to a stationary bulk tank for cooling. At the end of each tube is a cap, which the milker slips over each of the cow's teats, after washing them with warm water and disinfectant. When the power is turned on, a vacuum keeps the cap in place and draws the milk pulsating through the tube.

When milking is finished, the men sterilize the machines and pipes, leaving the cows placidly chewing their cuds.

PIGS

Next to the cow, the pig was probably the most useful animal on the old farm. At slaughtering time he became fresh pork, ham and bacon, pork chops, spareribs, pigs' feet, and headcheese, which was often the only meat the farmer had available during the long cold winters. Pigskin and hog bristles were useful in many ways, and farmers claimed that they used almost every part of a hog.

Hogs often were permitted to run wild through the woods, feeding on acorns and herbs. They grew so tough and lean that they were called razorbacks. Later they lived in pigpens, often filthy and dilapidated, and wallowed outside in muddy, garbage-strewn puddles. Such conditions frequently bred disease, since the pigs or their pens seldom were cleaned.

The modern piggery is a far different setting for pork production; it is either on clean pastureland or housed in clean, airy, efficient buildings. The cleaning now is done automatically. In some systems a swinging boom carrying water jets under seventy pounds of pressure circles the exercise area continually, sweeping the cement floor and flushing the waste down a drain to the manure spreader. In other systems floors are cleaned by mechanical drags.

The sow gives birth in a farrowing pen. Each pen has a curved rail, which forces her to lie with her teats facing the newborn piglets and prevents her from crushing them. The young stay on the insulated floor under the warmth of heat lamps, where they can reach their mother to nurse. Each sow averages two litters a year. After weaning— usually three to five weeks—the sows are removed from the nursery. The pigs remain in the same pen until they are ready to market.

Aids to Farming

IRRIGATION

In the mid-nineteenth century, as most of the good farmland east of the Mississippi was taken up, homesteaders moved westward into the Great Plains, where rain was more infrequent. When crops were burned out by drought, many farmers moved even farther west to California, Oregon, and the Southwest. There they found good climate and soil, but water was lacking.

The United States government and many of the states began constructing huge dams in the mountain canyons to supply water to the growing Western towns, to impound floodwaters to prevent washing out the lowlands, to provide a cheap source of power, and to irrigate the farms. Farmers became aware of the value of water, whereas those of a generation before had drained swamps, leveled hollows, and diverted streams to get more plowland. Within a few years irrigation brought remarkable changes; the valleys of Washington, Oregon, Idaho, and California became bountiful gardens where vegetables, citrus fruits, apples, grapes, cotton, and many other crops brought millions of dollars to the farmers and ranchers every year.

Planners of irrigation projects have found that a great deal of water in the big reservoirs is wasted by evaporation. Twenty-five million acre feet are sucked into the air in the United States every year. To cut evaporation, water engineers are experimenting with floating a thin film of cetyl alcohol, only one molecule thick, on the surface of the water to keep it from vaporizing into the air. This method is successful as long as strong winds do not sweep the film ashore.

Sometimes the water from rain or irrigation

seeps deep into the ground before plants can take it into their root systems. At an agricultural experiment station, the topsoil was scraped aside from the surface of a field, and a thin layer of hot asphalt was sprayed onto the subsoil. When the asphalt cooled, the topsoil was replaced and seeded. The water thus was prevented from sinking beneath the asphalt, out of the reach of the plant roots, resulting in a greatly increased yield of crops.

A desert can be made to grow food if only water can be brought to it. For centuries men have longed to use ocean water and make the deserts bloom. Today desalting plants are changing saltwater into fresh, sparkling drinking water.

Will farmers now be able to make the deserts produce food for the hungry of the world? That goal still seems a long way off, for many knotty problems remain unsolved. Desalting the enormous quantities of water needed for irrigation and piping the water long distances from the coast to the desert is too costly. What to do with the huge mountains of salt remaining after de-salting is also as yet unanswered.

However, researchers are hard at work. Perhaps atomic power may be applied to cut the cost, or some as yet undiscovered method of nullifying the salt content may be worked out. When the solutions are found, the American farmer doubt-less will be farming further the country's deserts.

WEED AND PEST CONTROL

The nineteenth-century farmer had only crude methods to protect his crops against insect pests and numberless weeds that destroyed his tender plants. Farmers dug trenches and filled them with burning oil to combat the swarms of locusts, which weighed perhaps 50,000 tons and were of-ten so dense they obscured the sun. These raven-ous insects could leave the fields in their path completely stripped. Farmers also burned out nests of tent caterpillars in fruit trees and

76

knocked the spotted potato bugs from potato plants into tin cans.

Those in the Great Plains saved their potato crops from the Colorado potato beetle with Paris Green, an arsenical poison, and treated their grain seed with copper sulfate against plant diseases. Also, crops were rotated, so that weeds thriving with a particular plant could not survive. However, the pest and weed controls of that day could not keep pace with the problems.

Some 10,000 species of insects are harmful to crops, livestock, or trees, and every crop has its special enemies, from boll weevils to corn rootworms and wheat stem sawflies. The farmer also has to battle 1500 kinds of nematodes (microscopic worms), 600 kinds of weeds, and 1500 types of plant diseases.

At different times and in different places new diseases suddenly appear or well-known ones increase and become dangerous. Livestock and poultry constantly are threatened by diseases that strike like lightning and spread as fast. Such killers as hoof-and-mouth disease, hog cholera, and many others can wipe out any unwary farmer's flocks and herds without the protection of various types of preventive measures.

Many chemical compounds have been developed to control the enemies of crops and livestock, and the American farmer spends nearly a billion dollars yearly on them. There are insecticides to destroy harmful insects, nematocides for nematodes, fungicides to control plant diseases, herbicides to kill weeds, and rodenticides to battle rats and other rodents. The Department of Agriculture carefully inspects and regulates every type of pesticide and studies its effect on plants and animals.

The farmer introduces pesticides and herbicides to his fields by spraying or dusting them with a power sprayer or spreading them from a low-flying airplane or helicopter, called a crop duster. Or the chemicals can be released from a seeder at the same time the field is being seeded.

The discovery of dinitro compounds proved

that herbicides could be designed to kill certain plants without harming others. In 1940's, the product 2,4-D was successful in controlling weeds on more than eighteen million acres of small grains and four and one-half million acres of corn within five years.

The use of herbicides in the early 1960's increased in three years from 6.7 million to 22.4 million dollars' worth. They controlled weeds on over seventy million acres of farmland, twenty-five million acres of corn, six million acres of cotton, three million acres of soybeans, twenty million acres of small grains, such as corn, sorghum, and rice, and seven million acres of pastureland. Insecticides protected thirty-two million acres of grains, twelve million acres of cotton, two million acres of vegetables, and about twenty million acres of other crops.

Without pesticides it is believed that from twenty-five to thirty percent of crops and livestock would be lost every year, the cost of food would rise fifty to seventy-five percent, the quality of vegetables, fruit, and meat would drop, and Eastern potatoes, peaches, and citrus fruits would be almost totally ravaged.

The well-known insecticide, DDT, is a chlorinated hydrocarbon, made up of carbon, hydrogen, and chlorine. There is considerable protest over its use, because of the poison's long-lasting effects and its buildup in the bodies of birds and fish and also in human beings. However, during the last twenty years DDT also has increased crop output per acre by a third, improving the quality of foods, and keeping costs down, while killing many insects that might transmit human diseases. Chemists now are working on compounds to replace DDT that will not damage other life.

Today researchers also are experimenting with sterilization to control certain pests. For instance, large numbers of male screwworms and Mediterranean fruit flies have been sterilized by radiation and released to mate. Since the females cannot produce eggs, their population is controlled.

Finally, there is the constant search for an insect, otherwise harmless, that will attack a pest insect or its eggs. The classic example is the Japanese wasp, imported into the United States. This insect destroys only the grub of the Japanese beetle, which had infested Eastern lawns. Another example is a beetle that has been brought from Australia to kill off the Klamath weed, which had made useless much rangeland.

Farm of the Future

During the next thirty years, world population is predicted to zoom as much as it has during the past million years, to an incredible six billion human beings. Food producers somehow will have to increase production of every type of food by huge amounts. If past history is any guide to the future, the American farmer will be equal to the task of filling the quotas needed to feed our people, exporting surpluses to areas that cannot grow enough food for themselves, and furnishing the know-how to improve and increase crops in countries less advanced.

Farmers then may grow 300 bushels of wheat an acre compared to today's 27, 175 bushels of soybeans instead of 24, and 30 tons of forage instead of 3. Each cow may give 30,000 pounds of milk compared to 8000 today, and a ten-months-old steer may produce 1000 pounds of prime beef instead of about 750.

Geneticists probably will remodel cornstalks to look like squatty pine trees, so they can absorb more sunlight, and the ears will grow out of the top, to make harvesting easier. They will be coaxed to yield 500 bushels per acre compared to the present national average of about 79.

A machine that bounces high-frequency sound waves through a steer's flesh will enable a cattle raiser to tell the exact shape and weight of every meat cut and will aid him in selecting the best breeding stock. Scientists are on the verge of releasing hormones for female animals that will make them produce twice as many offspring as they do now, and artificial insemination of ordinary cows with sperm from prize superior bulls will enable the bull to father 1000 calves during his lifetime instead of today's average of 10.

Meantime, milk that tastes like fresh cow's milk will be manufactured from vegetable products such as soybeans. Already some of the large dairies are marketing cream substitutes containing no dairy products at all.

The twenty-first-century farmhouse will have a control center with as many dials and levers as a jet plane's cockpit, from which electronic machines about the farm will be inspected and controlled. A battery of closed-circuit television receivers will permit the farmer to see and hear everything that is going on in the barns and other outbuildings at any time of the day or night. He may watch a calf being born or be warned of a cow with colic, all without leaving his house.

A multistory skyscraper will house the farm animals and poultry in completely controlled temperature and humidity. Flanking this building, a feed mill will mix automatically the type of feed each group of livestock requires and release it in proper quantities into feeding troughs at preset times. All waste from the barns will be flushed through pipes to the nearby fertilizer treatment plant, where it will be treated and dumped into the automatic manure spreader, while the water drained off is purified and reused.

Here and there will be huge transparent plastic domes, covering as much as ten acres or more, in which special crops are grown under computer-controlled conditions of temperature, humidity, irrigation, and fertilization.

Since the twenty-first-century farm will rely so extensively on machines, it will have a garage and machine shop, which might be another large plastic bubble to allow room to store the huge, expensive plows, reapers, mowers, harvesters, and tractors. Several well-trained automobile mechanics and electronics men will maintain them in good repair. There, too, will be the airdrome for the STOL planes and helicopters, the hover craft, and pesticide spreaders, as well as the usual farm trucks and pickups.

A big, all-purpose refrigeration plant will keep fruits chilled, quick-freeze vegetables after they

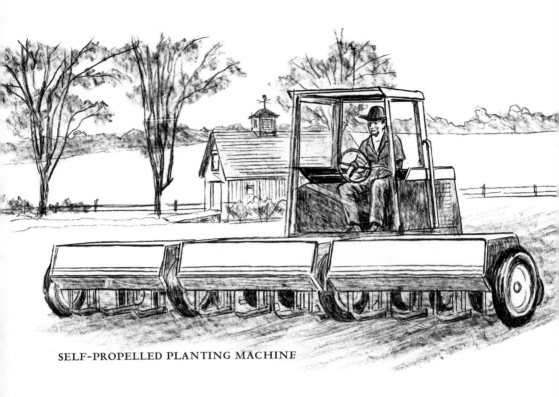

SELF-PROPELLED PLANTING MACHINE

are packaged, or preserve meat by cryogenic freezing (freezing at very low temperatures).

In the fields and orchards high-speed plows, with the plowshare's cutting edges energized by controlled vibrations and the blades kept scoured by compressed air, will turn over many furrows at once. Self-propelled planting machines with changeable seed plates will have four different systems for planting a variety of crops. As the

86

TRACTORS

seeds are planted, they also will be fertilized and protected with pesticides and herbicides.

Driverless tractors, powered by turbines or by nuclear engines fueled for the life of the tractor, will be put to work. They will be controlled by operating patterns programmed on magnetic tape and steered by sensing devices, which keep the tractor following any furrow pattern desired, or by wires buried underground at the edge of the field into which the tractor's controls are locked. Cabs on tractors with drivers will be air-conditioned, with light beams for night work and instrument panels to operate the elaborate machines they will be hauling.

After finishing work on a field, a big combine will be able to swivel its wheels ninety degrees, swing the cab around, and drive away at the speed of a trailer truck. Sensing devices will permit a picking machine to detect light-reflecting bolls of cotton, rejecting leaves, trash, or unripe bolls. A tomato picker will select ripe tomatoes electronically by their color, leaving the green ones to mature. Harvesting machines, which are now being developed, will cut, shell, package, and freeze vegetables right in the field.

By the year 2000, farmers may be using combination helicopters and hover craft to reach crops growing in rough or swampy country and to spray and harvest such fruit as cranberries. One

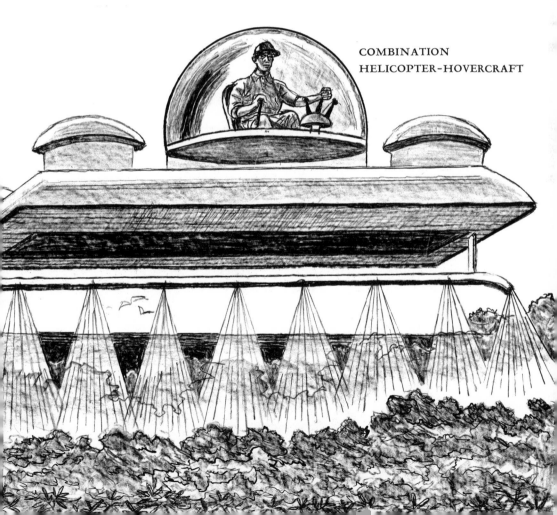

COMBINATION
HELICOPTER-HOVERCRAFT

method of harvesting apples might be to drive a machine between the rows of the orchard and strip the fruit from the trees by shaking or by compressed air. The apples drop onto a moving

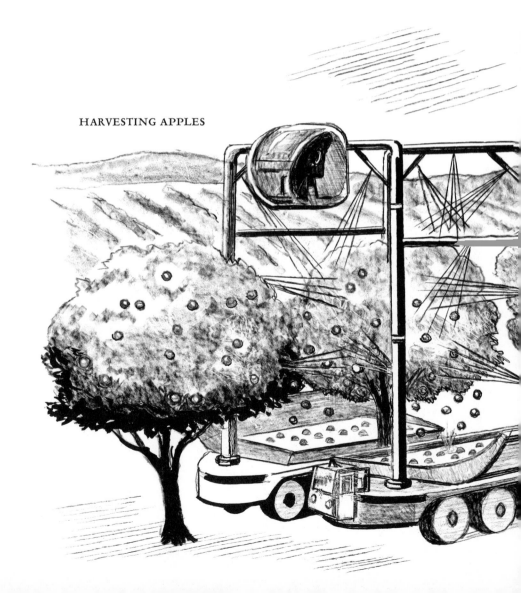

HARVESTING APPLES

belt that slides into a trailer, where they are sorted and packaged. The trailer then is lifted by a helicopter and flown to the warehouse.

A potential problem on the farm of the future

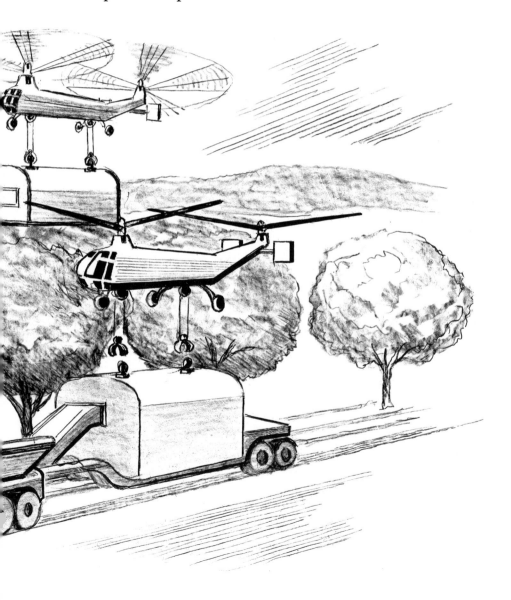

is that the soil will be packed down by the wheels of the heavy farm machines. Engineers feel this difficulty can be avoided by a bridge-type machine that spans the field, each end resting on a power unit running on a separate roadbed just outside the field. Planting, cultivating, and harvesting machines would travel back and forth in opposite directions along this overhead bridge, which would move ahead automatically at each pass.

In some cases, chain-reaction machines will be able to harvest one crop and at the same time prepare the ground, fertilize, and plant the next crop, all in one operation. With others, chemically coated seeds, pneumatically planted out of season by the farmer when his work load is light, will be kept dormant until germinating time arrives. Some seeds, like sugar beets, which have been pre-coated with fertilizers and insect chemicals, already are being planted.

Space satellites will be able to report on crop conditions throughout the world by taking photographs showing the kind and amount of light the earth reflects. They will spot insect infestations and plant diseases early, so that farmers can spray with low-cost chemicals or counterattack with helpful insects, light-ray traps, or other biological controls.

Scientists predict that soon they will be able to protect citrus fruits from temperatures far below freezing by chemical growth regulators, making the smudge pot out-of-date in the orange grove during frosts. Already chemicals are increasing the soybean yield dramatically by forcing more blossoms to mature.

Much of the food for the new billions of people in the next century probably will have to be produced from sources other than farmers' fields and orchards. A promising method of raising food is hydroponics, the growing of plants in water with fertilizers. The harvesting of various seaweeds and plants for food, which has been carried on for many years, especially in Japan, and the scientific farming of fish will increase the food supply. Huge refineries will produce rich proteins from plankton.

The farmer has come a long, long way since the pioneer days, far beyond the most imaginative colonist's wildest dreams. How far beyond the vision of the most forward-thinking American farmer of today will the farm of the next century be?